MOONJINMEDIA

Reprinted and Distributed by Creative Teaching Press 2013
First Published June, 2009
Published by Moonjinmedia Co., Ltd.
www.moonjin.com

Text © 2009 Moonjinmedia Co., Ltd.
Illustrations © 2009 Seoyoung Chung

ISBN 978-89-539-2702-5

e-CIP Homepage
http://www.nl.go.kr/cip.php
CIP: CIP2009001576

A-Hunting We will Go

Rozanne Lanczak Williams

Seoyoung Chung

A-hunting we will go.
A-hunting we will go.
We'll catch a **fox** and put him in a box,
And then we'll let him go!

A-walking we will go.
A-walking we will go.
We'll catch a bug and give her a hug,
And then we'll let her go!

A-sailing we will go.

A-sailing we will go.

We'll catch a goat and put him in a boat,

And then we'll let him go!

A-swimming we will go.
A-swimming we will go.
We'll catch a fish and put her on a dish,
And then we'll let her go!

A-riding we will go.
A-riding we will go.
We'll catch a snake and give him a cake,
And then we'll let him go!

A-hopping we will go.

A-hopping we will go.

We'll catch a frog and put her on a log,

And then we'll let her go!

A-flying we will go.
A-flying we will go.
We'll catch a bee and put him in a tree,
And then we'll let him go!